NEIL A. KJOS
PIANO LIBRARY

LEVEL TWO

Jeanine Yeager

New Age Piano

Fresh Impressions

Contents

ISBN 0-8497-9646-6

ABOUT THE COMPOSER

Jeanine Nellis Yeager has received national recognition for her fresh and appealing piano compositions for students. Her style has attracted a large number of followers who admire her expressive and improvisational style. A native of Dayton, Ohio, Jeanine Yeager attended the Cincinnati College Conservatory of Music. As an accompanist for the Conservatory dance department, she became skilled at keyboard improvisation. This love for improvisation is reflected in her compositions.

Mrs. Yeager completed her Bachelor of Music degree in piano at Capitol University and received her Master of Music degree in theory and composition from Ohio State University. Jeanine especially enjoys creating compositions that fit the personality and are designed to meet the individual needs of the student. Her expertise in composition enables her to create motivational and exciting pieces that encourage students to excel. Her professional affiliations include memberships in Sigma Alpha Iota and The Dayton Music Club.

THE NEIL A. KJOS PIANO LIBRARY

The **Neil A. Kjos Piano Library** is a comprehensive series of piano music in a wide variety of musical styles. The library is divided into eleven levels and will provide students with a complete performance experience in both solo and ensemble music. Teachers will find the carefully graded levels appropriate when choosing repertoire for evaluations, auditions, festivals, and examinations. Included in the **Neil A. Kjos Piano Library**:

Preparatory Level - Level Ten

Piano Repertoire: Baroque & Classical
Piano Repertoire: Romantic & 20th Century
Piano Repertoire: Etudes
Music of the 21st Century
New Age Piano
Jazz Piano
One Piano Four Hands
Music for Christmas

PREFACE

New Age Piano from the **Neil A. Kjos Piano Library** gives piano students of all ages and performance abilities an opportunity to explore the sounds and nuances of the expressive "New Age" style. In each volume, pianists are presented with an ample selection of music in a variety of tempos and styles. The carefully graded compositions ensure steady and thorough progress in "New Age " styling as pianists advance. These motivational solos may be assigned for study and performance with any method or course of study.

NOTES ON "NEW AGE"

New Age is an illusive term for an equally illusive type of music. Drawing from the musical influence of the Impressionists in combination with contemporary elements, *New Age Music* presents a vague expression of impressions with an interplay of color. Closely aligned with the music of Debussy, *New Age Music* offers the performer a wealth of coloristic sound combinations. Compositions are usually "flowing and resonant" and interpretive. This contemporary genre of music often deals with natural phenomena and provides an impression of nature. *New Age Music* engages the listener to experience a feeling or mood, frequently one of introspection, peace and calm, or by contrast evokes feelings of high energy.

NOTES ON THIS VOLUME

This collection includes "flowing and resonant" pieces. For this reason the damper pedal is used throughout the book. The pieces are written so that the Level Three student can move easily using the entire keyboard. In order to avoid too harsh a combination of resulting blending harmonies and overtones, it is recommended that the student play with a gentle, light touch, except in loud passages where a harmonic "blend" works. One of the special charms found in this collection is the magic potential for colorful sound blendings.

CHANT

Jeanine Yeager

Smoothly, unhurried ($\quad$ = 96)

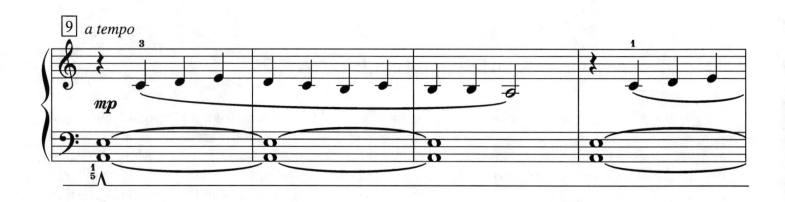

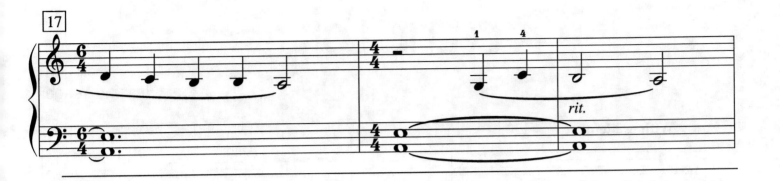

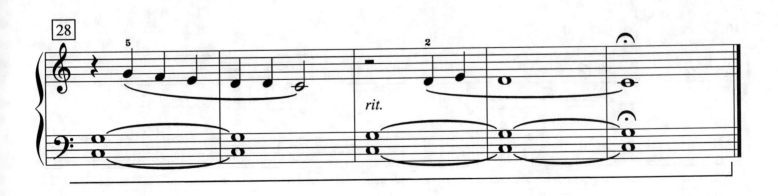

CELTIC LORE

Jeanine Yeager

With excitement (♩ = 120)

Pedal tone D

© 1997 Neil A. Kjos Music Company

WP519

FAR TIME

Jeanine Yeager

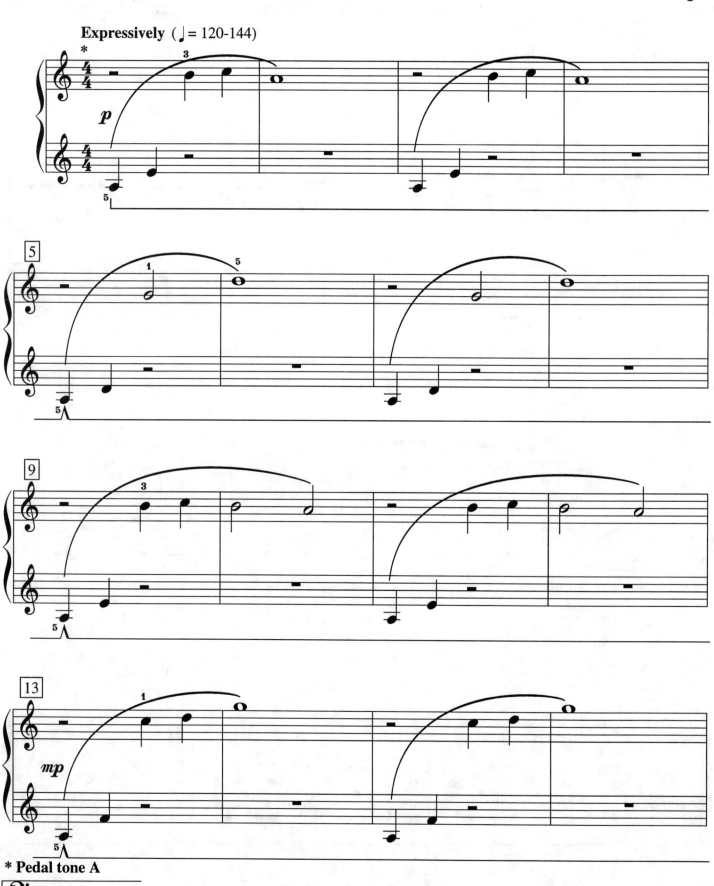

* Pedal tone A

WP519

SIMPLICITY

Jeanine Yeager

Gently (♩ = 92)

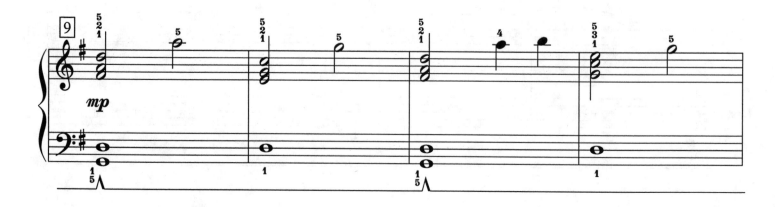

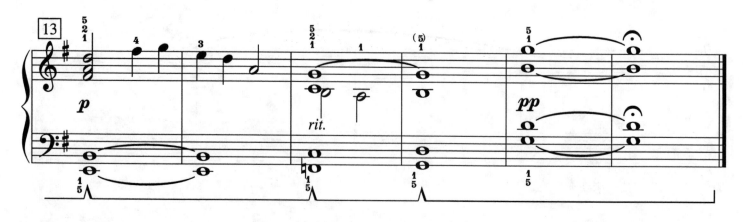

© 1997 Neil A. Kjos Music Company

LOST IN TIME

Jeanine Yeager

* **Pedal tone A**

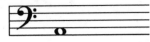

© 1997 Neil A. Kjos Music Company

WP519

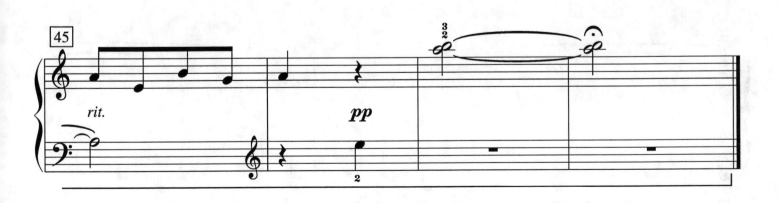

WIND SONG

Jeanine Yeager

Gently (♩ = 138)

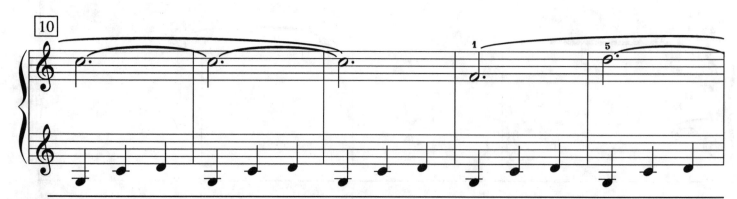

* Pedal tone low C for measures 1– 40

© 1997 Neil A. Kjos Music Company

WP519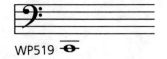

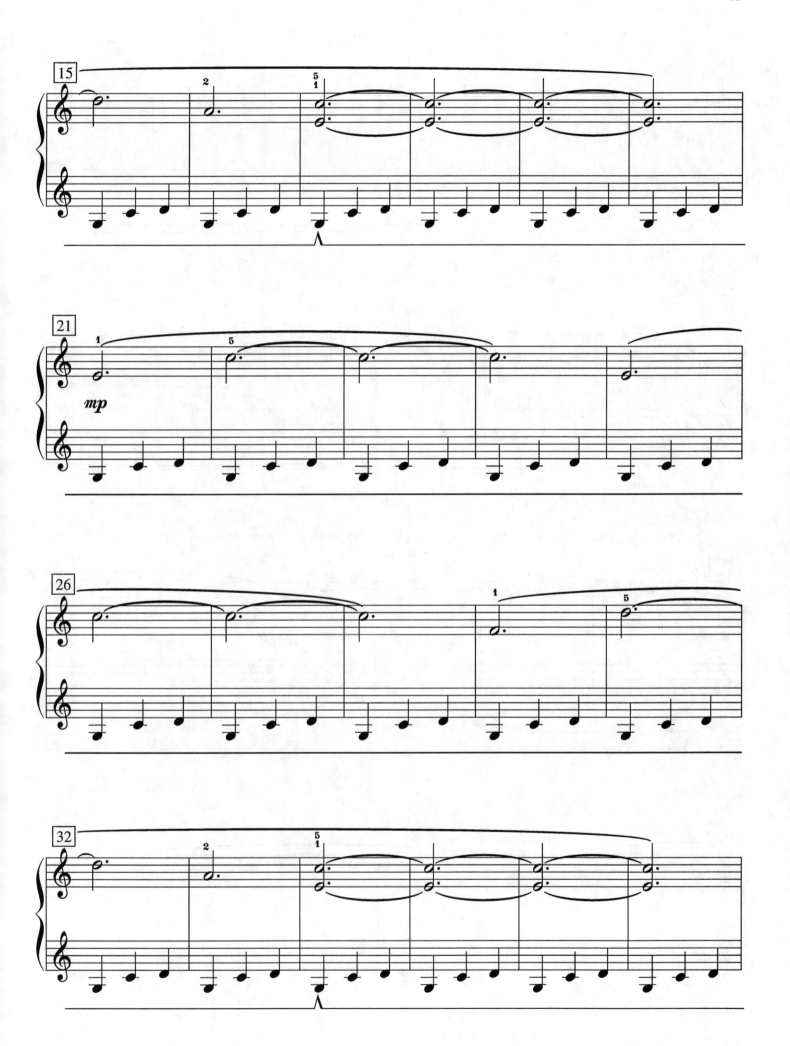

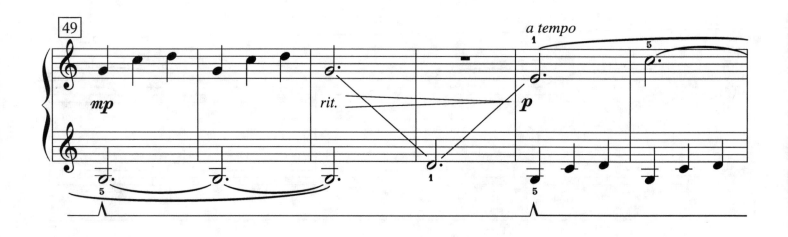

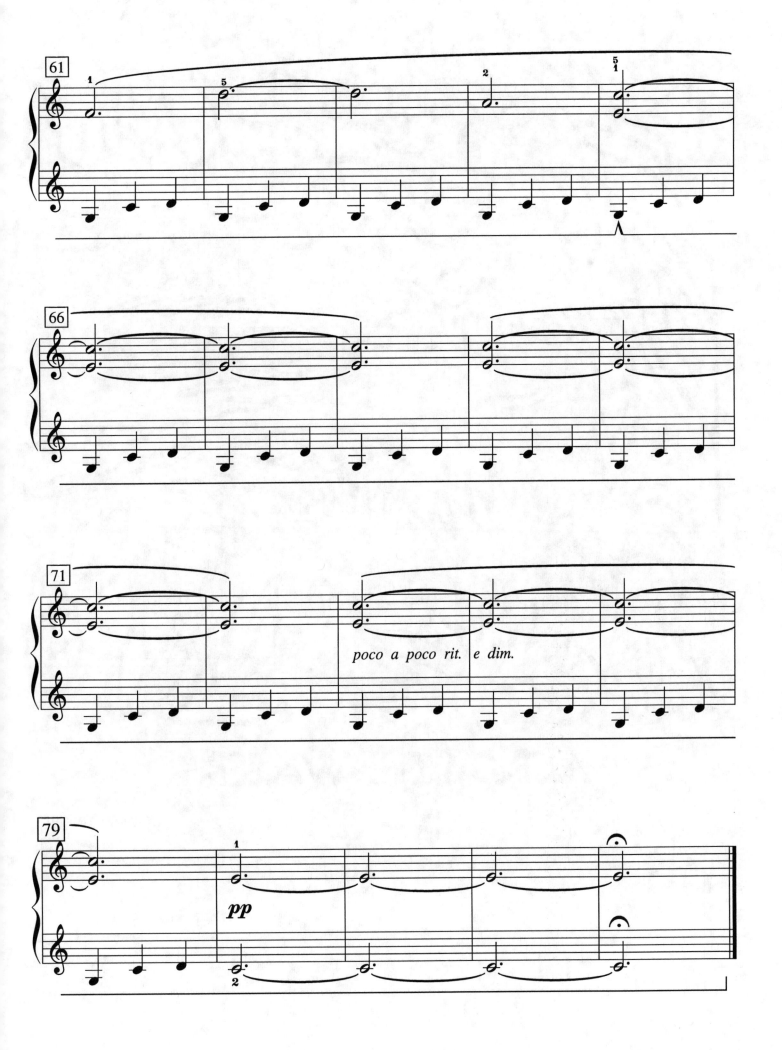

poco a poco rit. e dim.

pp

ACROSS THE WATER

Jeanine Yeager

Gently (♩ = 80)

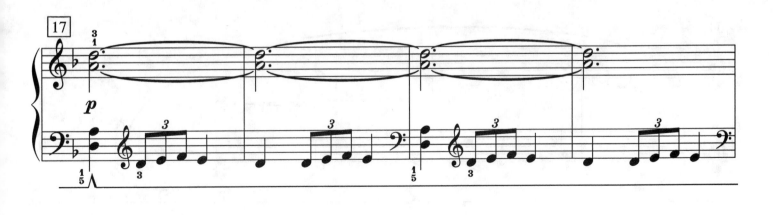

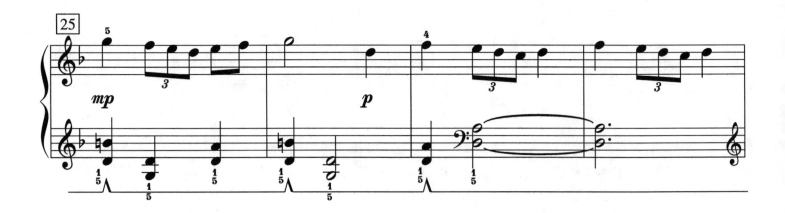

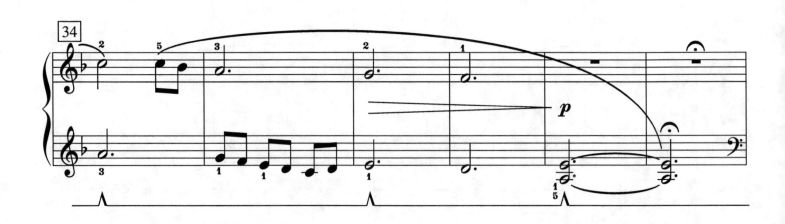

FREE FLOW

Jeanine Yeager

Smoothly ($\bullet$ = 52)

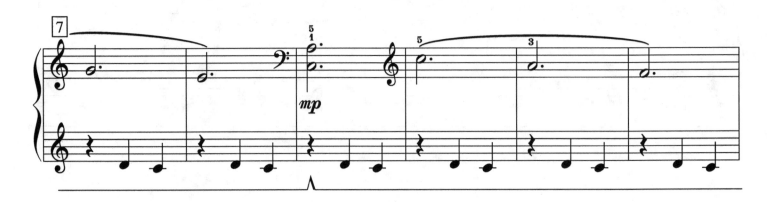

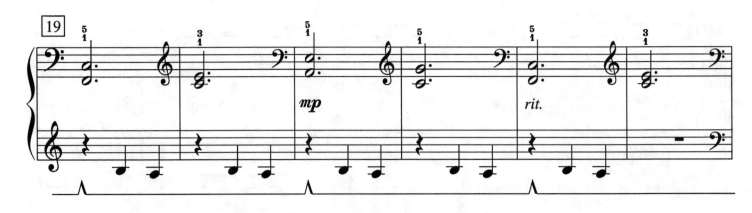

© 1997 Neil A. Kjos Music Company

A PEACEFUL PLACE

Jeanine Yeager

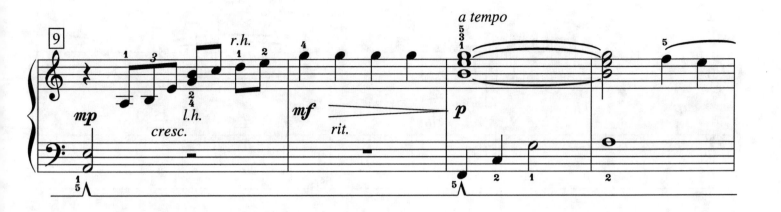

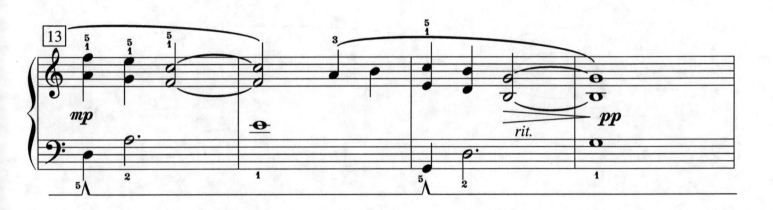

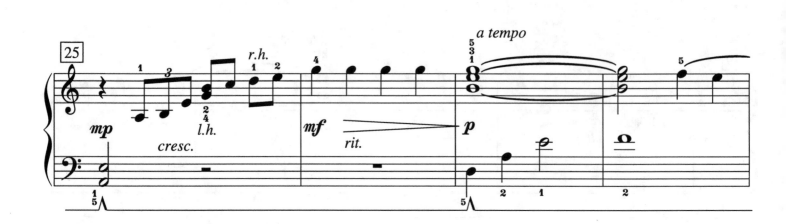

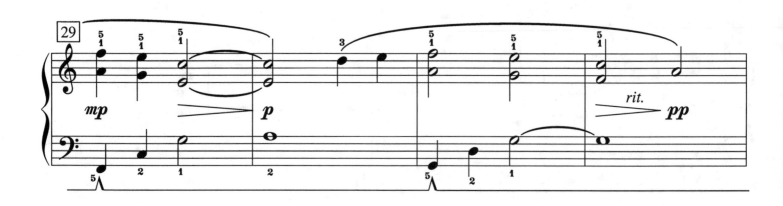

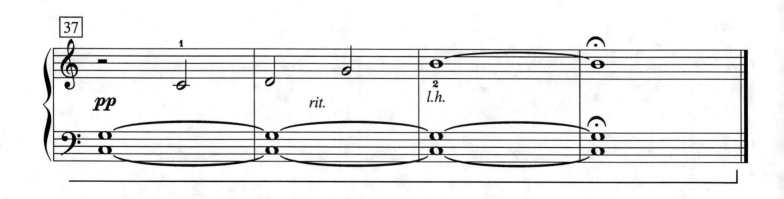

WILLOWS

Jeanine Yeager

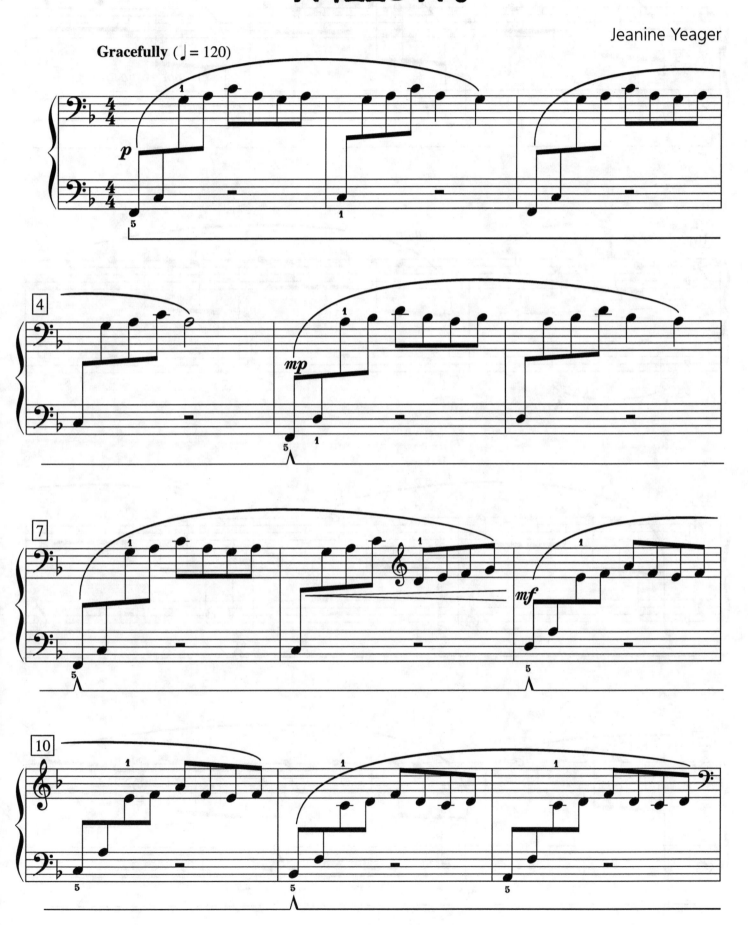

WILD RIDE

Jeanine Yeager

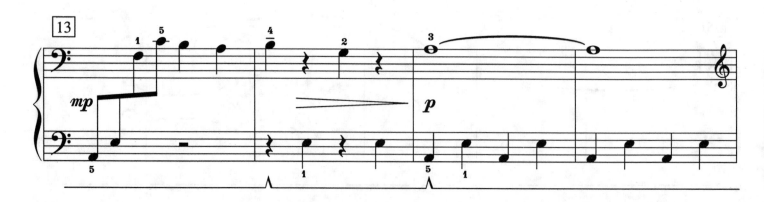

© 1997 Neil A. Kjos Music Company